Disney

POCAHONTAS

At a busy London dock, settlers seeking freedom and riches prepared to board a ship that would take them far away to a new land.

Whilst others bid their families a teary farewell, John Smith stood alone on deck, eager for his next adventure. Then, John Ratcliffe, the greedy governor of the new settlement, strode on board.

The journey was treacherous. During a storm, Smith rescued a young man named Thomas from falling overboard. But Ratcliffe reminded the crew of the new lives waiting for them. "Don't lose heart, men!" he told them. "Remember what awaits us there – freedom... prosperity... the adventure of our lives!"

Across the Atlantic, Native American warriors, led by Chief Powhatan, had returned from battle, victorious. He searched the gathered tribe for his beloved daughter, Pocahontas.

As usual, however, Pocahontas was out exploring with her friends Meeko the raccoon and Flit the hummingbird.

Later that day, Pocahontas went to see Grandmother Willow, a wise old tree who dwelt in an enchanted glade. Pocahontas was seeking advice about a dream she'd had.

"I'm running through the woods and then, right there in front of me, is an arrow. As I look at it, it starts to spin. It spins faster and faster and faster until suddenly it stops," she described.

Grandmother Willow thought the dream was trying to tell Pocahontas which path in life she should take.

Suddenly, Pocahontas felt a breeze, so she climbed high into Grandmother Willow's branches, trying to hear what the wind might be telling her.

Looking out over the treetops, she saw white clouds billowing in the distance. She had never seen such strange clouds, until she realised it was a ship!

Pocahontas watched the ship come in, and even before the anchor had dropped, Smith leapt ashore. He climbed a tree to view the magnificent new land, as Pocahontas watched him curiously from afar. But he sensed a presence watching him, and he turned round. Pocahontas quickly hid, and Flit distracted the new stranger from seeing her.

At the village, Chief Powhatan wanted to know what the ship's arrival might mean. The medicine man threw a handful of powder into the fire and smoke arose from the flames, revealing warriors whose weapons shot fire and thunder.

Disturbed, the Chief sent men to observe the newcomers. "Let's hope they don't intend to stay," he told his tribe.

Back in the forest, Smith was resting at the edge of the river, when he saw a shape move in the mist. At first, he raised his weapon, but then his eyes met with Pocahontas. She ran from him at first, but as he caught up with her a light breeze swirled around them and Pocahontas remembered what Grandmother Willow had said – listen with her heart and the spirits would guide her.

Little did they know, one of the warriors had returned to the village from the settlers' camp, having been shot in the leg by the intruders.

Chief Powhatan was enraged. "We will fight this enemy, but we cannot do it alone," he declared. "Send messengers to every village in our nation. And we'll call on our brothers to help us fight."

Pocahontas and Smith, unaware of the conflict between their peoples, slowly started getting to know each other. Smith told her all about London, while Pocahontas showed him how all parts of nature are alive and connected. Suddenly, they heard drumbeats echoing through the forest. Pocahontas ran off to investigate what they could be.

Later, Pocahontas was gathering corn when Smith emerged from the forest again. Pocahontas sneaked off with him, asking her concerned friend not to tell anyone where she was going.

Pocahontas and Smith sat together in the enchanted glade, and when Smith told Pocahontas about the settlers' search for gold, she told him she had never seen any. Smith realised his men would never find what they were looking for.

Just then, Grandmother Willow revealed her face in the old tree. This startled Smith, but the enchanted tree quickly reassured him. “My bark is worse than my bite,” she joked. She looked at Smith more closely. “He has a good soul,” she said to Pocahontas. “And he’s handsome, too!”

When she returned home, Pocahontas was alarmed to find warriors from many villages assembled, ready for battle.

She begged her father to talk rather than fight, but he was certain the intruders did not want to talk.

"But if one of them did want to talk, you would listen to him, wouldn't you?" she asked.

"Of course I would, but it is not that simple," he replied.

Meanwhile, Smith arrived back at the settlement to find Ratcliffe preparing for war. "Smith! Where have you been?" he exclaimed.

Smith tried to explain the Native Americans were friendly, and he had met one who told him there was no gold, but Ratcliffe wouldn't listen.

That night, Pocahontas met Smith in the enchanted glade and asked him to speak with her father. Smith explained that it wouldn't do any good. "When two sides want to fight, nothing can stop them," he said. Suddenly, Grandmother Willow dipped a vine into the water.

"The ripples…" said Pocahontas.

"So small at first, then look how they grow," said the tree. Smith understood that he had to try and help, and agreed to meet the Chief.

Pocahontas and Smith embraced, but as they kissed, a warrior from Pochahontas' village attacked Smith with a dagger. At the same time, Smith's friend, Thomas, appeared in the glade and shot the warrior.

Other members of the tribe soon caught up and dragged Smith away, thinking he had shot their friend.

Thomas stayed hidden until it was safe to go back and tell Ratcliffe what had happened.

Smith was condemned by the tribe and tied up. Horrified, Pocahontas protested, but the Chief told his daughter she had shamed him.

Pocahontas went into the hut where Smith was imprisoned and told him it would have been better if they'd never met. "I'd rather die tomorrow then live a hundred years without knowing you," he told her.

Filled with despair, Pocahontas sat with Grandmother Willow, as Meeko handed her Smith's compass. The arrow was spinning! She knew it was a sign from her dream, but when the arrow stopped, it was pointing towards the morning light.

"It's not too late, child. Let the spirits of the earth guide you," the enchanted tree advised.

At sunrise, the Native Americans moved in procession, just as the armed settlers marched through the forest. Suddenly, Pocahontas threw herself on top of Smith. "If you hurt him, you'll have to hurt me, too!" she said. Everyone stared in stunned silence.

"Look around you," she continued. "This is where the path of hatred has brought us. This is the path I choose, father. What will be yours?"

As the wind swirled, Chief Powhatan spoke. "My daughter speaks with the wisdom beyond her years. She comes with courage and understanding... from this day forward, if there is to be more killing, it will not start with me. Release him."

The warriors lowered their weapons, but Ratcliffe ordered the settlers to fire! Thankfully, the settlers saw how Ratcliffe had acted out of greed, but when they lowered their weapons, the enraged governor grabbed a gun and fired.

Smith jumped in front of Chief Powhatan and the bullet meant for the Chief hit him instead. His own men dragged Ratcliffe back to the ship in disgrace.

The tribe took care of Smith, but Pocahontas knew he needed to return home to survive. "You are always welcome among our people," Chief Powhatan told Smith.

Smith asked Pocahontas to go with him, and her father told her to choose her own path, but Pocahontas knew her people needed her. She chose to stay. "No matter what happens, I'll always be with you. Forever," she said.

Pocahontas ran to the top of a cliff, so she could watch the ship set sail back to London. She felt the wind swirl around her, the same wind carrying Smith away – the same wind that embraced them both.